THE MAGIC OF
BLUE

The Color Books are dedicated to the Rainbow Child in all of you

Series concept by Ayman Sawaf
Copyright © 1995 by Enchanté Publishing
MRS. MURGATROYD Character copyright © 1993 by Enchanté
MRS. MURGATROYD™ is a trademark of Enchanté

Written by Neysa Griffith.
Character created by Steven Duarte.
Illustrated by Deborah Morse.
Edited by Gudrun Höy, Anne Sheldon and Linda Hull.
Book design by Romney Lange.

Enchanté Publishing
P.O. Box 620471
Woodside, CA 94062

Printed in Singapore

Library of Congress Cataloging-in-Publication Data
Griffith, Neysa
The magic of blue / written by Neysa Griffith; character created by Steven Duarte; illustrated by Deborah Morse. - lst ed.
    p.   cm.
Summary: Playful verses and illustrations invite children to enter the magical world of colors.
ISBN 1-56844-029-4 : $6.95
1. Blue—Juvenile poetry. 2. Colors—Juvenile poetry.
3. Children's poetry. American [1. Blue—Poetry. 2. Color–Poetry. 3. American poetry.]
I. Neysa Griffith. II. Morse, Deborah, ill.   III. Title.
PS3557.R4893M276   1995
811' .54—dc20   94-49071

First Edition
10 9 8 7 6 5 4 3 2 1

THE MAGIC OF
BLUE

Written by Neysa Griffith
Illustrated by Deborah Morse

enchanté Publishing

Blowing blue bubbles into the breeze,
gliding on air with delightful ease.
Daydreaming underneath the trees,
doing and thinking whatever you please.

Gazing toward the clear blue sky.
Bluebirds sailing, way up high.
Watching fluffy clouds float by.
Imagine what it's like to fly.

That cloud looks like a unicorn,
with wild blue mane and a silver horn.
Taking you on a magic ride,
the wind whistling at your side.

Soaring above snow-capped mountains
and crystal clear, cascading fountains.
Over icy lands of arctic blue,
where an Eskimo lives in a frosty igloo.

Forget-me-nots and big bluebells.
Tossing coins in wishing wells.
Blue is honest, blue is wise.
True blue friends who don't tell lies.

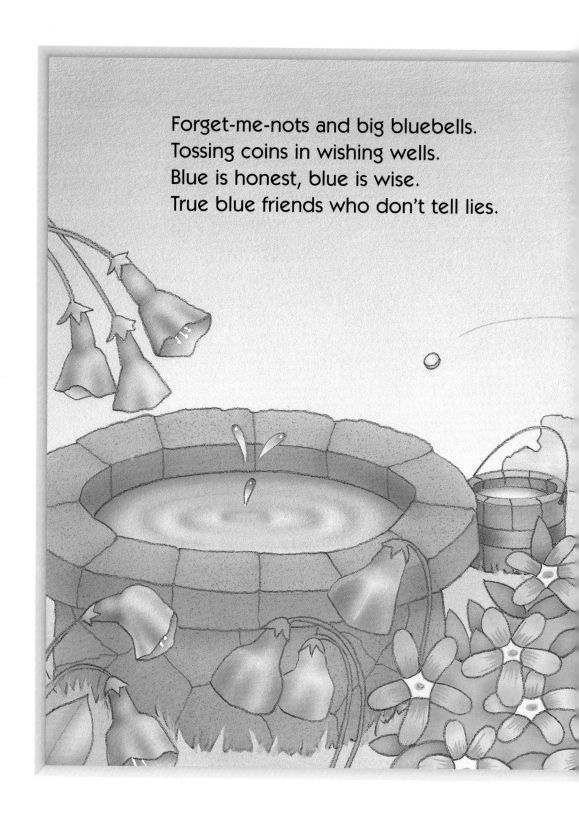

Cowboys and cowgirls wear denim duds,
and wash their jeans in soapy blue suds.

Native Americans sit around the fire
as smoke signals rise higher and higher.
Roasting blue corn, naturally grown.
Making jewelry from turquoise stone.

Aquamarine is the blue of the sea,
where friendly dolphins swim happy and free.
Smart, small fish swim swiftly in schools,
their slippery skin like shimmering jewels.

Blue diamond drops of falling rain
splashing on the window pane.
The quiet time of being alone,
reading a book or writing a poem.

The soothing song of the big blue whale
tells an ancient, peaceful tale.

A sparkling sapphire in twilight space.
Planet earth is a wonderful place.

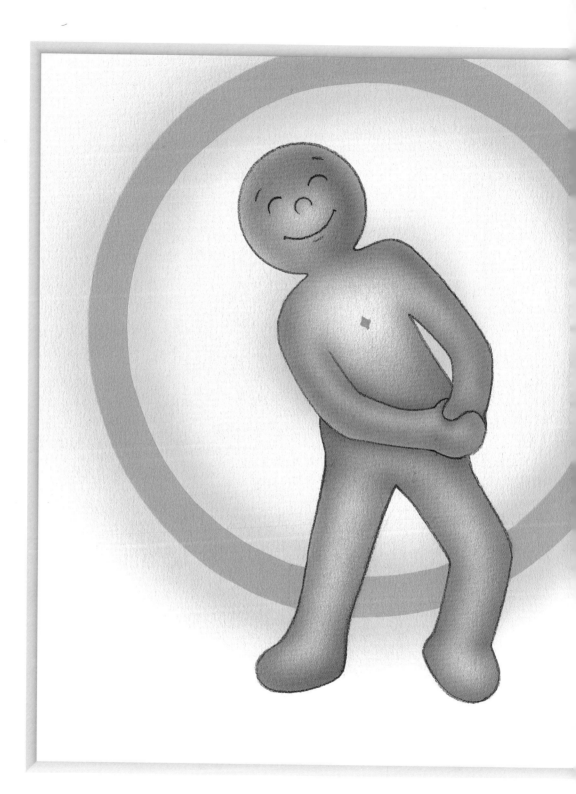

The magic of blue lives inside of you.
It can happily help you in all that you do.
To make blue your friend,
close your eyes and pretend...

You're watching the blue moon rise in the night,
relaxed in the glow of its luminous light.
In the distance you see a treasure quite grand,
a bright blue bottle sticking out of the sand.

A pop of the cork and a genie appears,
to grant all your wishes and erase all your fears.
Reminding you that dreams do come true.
Anything can happen... just be true to you!

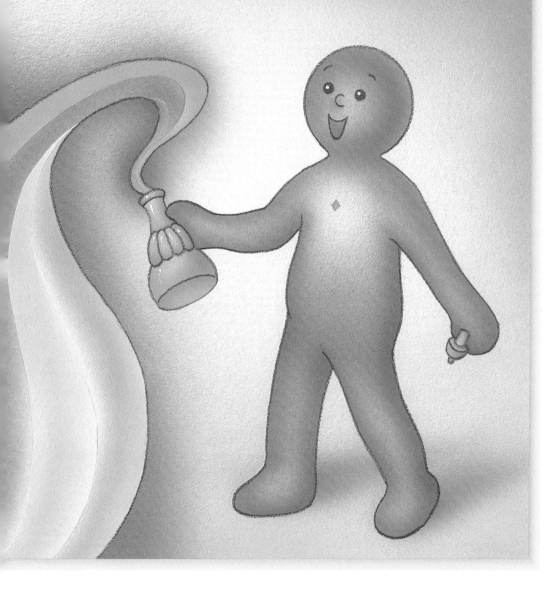

Enchanté books are dedicated to enhancing the general well-being of children by encouraging them to use their own imagination and creativity to explore their thoughts and feelings. Each story is a symbolic journey into the magical world of self, where children discover the power they have within. Enchanté offers high quality hardcover picture books with accompanying activity books and parents' guides which include:

And Peter Said Goodbye
Exploring Grief
Exploring Grief With Your Child

Painting the Fire
Exploring Anger
Exploring Anger With Your Child

Red Poppies for a Little Bird
Exploring Guilt
Exploring Guilt With Your Child

The Rainbow Fields
Exploring Loneliness
Exploring Loneliness With Your Child

Nightmares in the Mist
Exploring Fear
Exploring Fear With Your Child

William's Gift
Exploring Hurt
Exploring Hurt With Your Child

Knight-time for Brigitte

For more information call:
1-800-473-2363

or (415) 529-2100
fax # (415) 851-2229